The Giant of Aran
belongs to:

_____

For my friend Sonia
- M.F.

For my mother Dorothy and my sisters Victoria May & Susan Anne
- P.L.

Text copyright © 2013 Mel Fisher
Illustrations copyright © 2013 Patricia Ludlow

First published in Ireland by O'Donnell Press 2013
12 Coolemoyne Park, Jordanstown, Co. Antrim BT37 0RP
Telephone: 028 9096 6493
Email: b.odonnell93@ntlworld.com
www.odonnellpress.com

Special thanks to Paul Porter & Heather Gracey

A CIP catalogue record of this book is available from the British Library.

Printed in Ireland by GPS Colour Graphics Ltd.

ISBN 978-0-9575910-0-4

1 2 3 4 5 6 7 8 9 10

O'DONNELL PRESS

the Giant of Aran

Mel Fisher & Patricia Ludlow

Freckles sat on Salthill beach staring out at sea. Swirling grey clouds over Galway Bay threatened rain and Freckles was lost for something to do.

THUD! Freckles jumped as a large, dirty and rather smelly foot stomped down beside him.

"Graaaaah!" grunted the enormous giant, as he grinned down at his best friend. He pointed to the islands sitting at the end of the bay and began to run on the spot.

"A race to Aran! What a great idea," said Freckles excitedly. But then he looked the giant up and down and slowly scratched his head. This was going to be tough for the Aran Islands looked very far away and he was only a very little leprechaun.

Freckles began to puzzle how he could beat his giant friend. A smile spread across his face as he muttered under his breath, "A boat! Yes, of course. I will build a boat." He ran along the beach looking for driftwood when he stumbled over an old picnic basket.

"WOW! This is perfect." thought Freckles. Using his belt and shoelaces he strapped some wood onto the basket, tied a picnic rug up as a sail and smiled proudly at his creation. With that strong wind he would surely beat his giant friend over to the Aran Islands.

The giant doubled over in laughter, **"Ha, ha, ha!"** he bellowed. He pointed to his big strong legs and raised his arms in victory. The giant was sure he would beat this little leprechaun. Drawing a picture of the three islands in the sand he placed an X on Inishmore, the largest island.

"Ok, first to Dun Aengus Fort on Inishmore is the winner!" said Freckles. The giant gave the thumbs up as he nodded in agreement.

Noon came and sunshine peeped through the clouds. The two friends stood on the beach ready to start. A rainbow arched through the sky leading the way to Aran.

Then a seagull cried and they were off. Sea water sprayed everywhere as they charged into the waves.

"You can't catch me!" taunted Freckles as an enormous gust of wind billowed his sail. The giant just grinned as he powered through the water.

Seagulls flew in from the surrounding cliffs. Dolphins
clicked and seals barked causing quite a hullabaloo.

The excitement was electric! Freckles and the giant were equal! Suddenly the wind died down and the boat's sail hung limply from the mast. In dismay Freckles watched the giant disappear in a wake of white surf.

"Oh no!" shouted Freckles as he began to paddle frantically. Freckles' hopes of winning disappeared as water started spurting into the boat and he began to sink. "Help!" yelled Freckles at the top of his voice.

"Click, click, click."

Freckles heard a dolphin close by. A surge of power pushed him out of the water high into the air. The dolphin jumped right over the rainbow and Freckles seized his chance to win. Leaping from the dolphin to the rainbow he slid towards Aran's Inishmore.

"Wheeeeeeee!" he shouted as he tickled the giant's ears with his feet on the way past, "Can't catch me now!"

As the giant reached for the leprechaun he lost his balance. Freckles watched in horror as his giant friend fell, his head hitting the soft sand of Kilmurvey Beach. The giant lay still for a moment. But realising he was first to Inishmore he jumped up in delight; he was sure he had won.

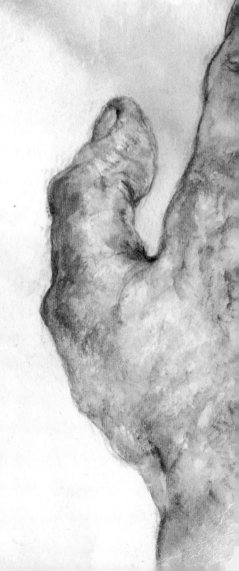

Freckles could see a pot gleaming with gold coins at the end of the rainbow and it was just beside the old fort. As he whizzed towards it he yelled, "Don't forget, it's first to Dun Aengus Fort."

CRASH! Freckles landed in the middle of the gold with a huge grin across his face. "Yippeeeeee!" Oh, how he loved gold.

One step took the giant to the top of the cliff and he stared at the little leprechaun in disbelief. Freckles smiled smugly and asked, "What about a ride home, my friend?"
The giant snorted and pointed to the pot of gold.
He wanted all the gold in exchange for the ride home.

"Oh alright!" moaned Freckles grumpily.

The giant tucked the pot of gold under his arm.
He lifted the cheeky little leprechaun, threw him onto
his shoulders and started the long walk back to Salthill
beach. With every step the giant grinned at his fortune
and with every step the crafty leprechaun slipped
another gold coin into his pocket!

Enjoy more great picture books from
O'Donnell Press

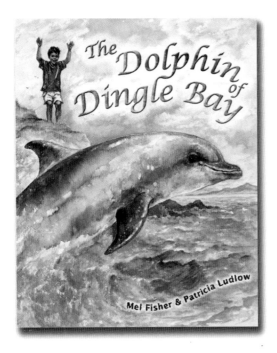

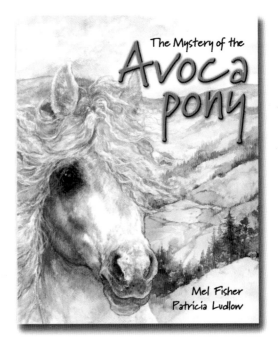

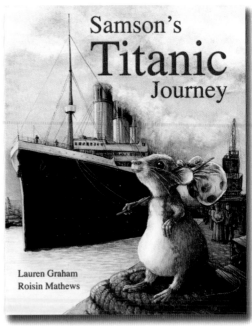

Visit: www.odonnellpress.com